Peacocks
Past and Present

By

Michael Roberts

Edited and Illustrated by

Sara Roadnight

Photography by

Michael Roberts,
Dennis Aron
and Dennis Erdman

Published by Gold Cockerel Books
ISBN 0947870 415

Printed by Quorum Print Services Ltd,
Units 3&4, Lansdown Industrial Estate, Cheltenham, GL51 8PL
Tel: 01242 584984   Website: www.quorumprint.co.uk
E-mail: info@quorumprint.co.uk

Contents

Acknowledgements

Many thanks must be given to the following people and organisations for their assistance without which this book would not have been possible.

British Museum
Dennis Erdman
Discover India
Derek Newberry
Father Peter of the church of St Peter, Capernaum
Guruvinder Sachdev of the Indian Tourist Board
Brian and Morag Johns
Quinton Spratt

Introduction

My first encounter with a peacock was at Warwick Castle near Stratford-on-Avon when I was a small boy. I remember being entranced by its rustling display and its boldness despite all the people gathered round. A few years later on a visit to Longleat, the home of Lord Bath, I was able to see White peafowl for the first time. Peafowl were a rarity outside zoos and stately homes in the early 1950s.

I later kept some of these birds at the Domestic Fowl Trust and was able to study them at first hand. Occasionally the hens used to jump out over the 6ft perimeter fence to look for a nesting place in the hedge, but they didn't last long as the area round the fence was overrun with foxes. I was eventually left with one cock bird who became such a thief at the picnic tables that I had to move him on.

Peafowl are easy to keep, you just need to have the right conditions to enjoy them in.

Michael Roberts and Sara Roadnight,
Kennerleigh, Devon.
June 2003

'Alexandras', two types of sea trout fishing fly. Peacock feathers are found in these as well as several other kinds of fly such as 'Coachman', 'Coch-y-Bondu', 'Peacock and Grouse', 'Hardie's Favourite' and 'Red Palmer'.

Burmese flag incorporating a peacock in its design during the time of British rule in Burma.

Peacocks were associated with the goddesses Hera and Juno and were sometimes portrayed on Roman coins. The lady shown borne aloft on a peacock is Paulina, wife of Verus Maximus, circa 235–238 AD.

Various heraldic crests belonging to old English and Scottish families including the Sankeys, the Chichesters, the Bournes and the Arbuthnots.

Chapter 1
Peacocks through the Ages

Throughout history peacocks have been linked with resurrection and immortality in all the great religions of the world. It is the male bird's vivid colours, its ability to regrow its train feathers and its durable cooked flesh (mentioned later) that connect it with renewal and everlasting life. As with most things religious there is no lack of documentation on the subject. A simple but touching example can be seen in the catacombs of Rome where there remains a faded image of two peacocks standing at the head and foot of a tomb with the single inscription: Cornelius Martyr.

One of the earliest known depictions of a peacock comes from the Indus valley which lies roughly between India and Pakistan. Harappan burial pottery has been found here dating back to 1900 BC. The dead were cremated and their ashes and bones put in pots with lids. Around the shoulders of these pots or urns were painted very stylized peacocks, suns and stars.

Harappan burial urn

There is an early mention of peacocks in the Bible, first in I Kings chapter 10 verse 22, and repeated in II Chronicles chapter 9 verse 21: "Once in three years came the navy of Tharshish, bringing gold and silver, ivory and apes and peacocks." This is part of the account of Bilquis, the Queen of Sheba's visit to King Solomon (970 – 931 BC). Although it is supposedly just a legend, the story is repeated in some detail in the Koran: "When she entered the Palace, she had

7

taken the polished floor to be water, and lifted her skirt. . . ." Many centuries later the mystic teacher Ibn Arabi (1165 – 1240 AD) painted a wonderful picture in his work Tarjuman al-ashwaq: "On the day of parting they did not saddle the full grown reddish camels, until they had mounted the peacocks upon them. Peacocks with murderous glances and sovereign power, thou would fancy that each was Bilquis on her throne of pearls."

King Solomon receiving the Queen of Sheba, by Edward Poynter, 1890. By courtesy of the Art Gallery, New South Wales, Australia.

The Reverend J.G. Wood in his book "Bird Life of the Bible" 1887, writes about the connection between peacocks and King Solomon, and the similarities between Hebrew and Cingalese names: "In the identification of any animal, much must necessarily depend on the country in which it is found. Now India and Ceylon are identified as the lands visited by Solomon's ships. In the latter island are found gold, silver, ivory, apes and peacocks, and it is remarkable that the Cingalese name for peacock is so similar to the Hebrew word, that we have every reason to believe that the word 'tucciyim' or 'tuyeyim' is in reality a Hebraic form of the Cingalese 'tokei'. A similar resemblance of name occurs in the Hebrew and Cingalese terms for ape and elephant."

By 500 BC trade with India and Ceylon (Sri Lanka) had been well established by the Phoenicians, the Greeks and the Romans. There is plenty of evidence for this in southern India, and it was said that peacocks had reached Athens by 450 BC and had been kept on the island of Samos even before that. Alexander the Great is alleged to have sent some to his mentor and teacher Aristotle (384 – 322 BC) but I can find no record of this. Certainly Aristotle wrote about peacocks, saying: "Those who rear these birds place the eggs for incubation beneath domestic fowls; because the peacock flies at and torments the hen when she is sitting; for which reason some of the wild birds make their escape from the males before they begin to lay and sit. They place only two eggs under domestic fowls for these are all that they can hatch and bring out." (The hens in those days must have been quite small, probably some form of bantam.)

Aristotle did not mention white peacocks in his writings so perhaps he had never heard of them. It was thought that white peacocks were only seen in European countries although Aldrovandi (1522 – 1605 AD) states that these birds were to be found on the island of Madeira. The French writer and naturalist Buffon (1707 – 1788 AD) wondered whether the climate affected the colour of peafowl in the same way that hares, stoats and ptarmigan became white in winter!

A White peacock displaying

9

When the Emperor Asoka of India converted to Buddism in the third century BC he decreed that: "not more than two peacocks and one gazelle should be killed for the royal table and not every day." By the end of his reign he had forbidden the slaughter of any living thing.

In Greek mythology the peacock is mentioned in connection with Zeus's jealous wife Hera. Zeus had fallen in love with Io, the daughter of the river god Inachus, and to avoid being discovered by his wife he turned Io into a white heifer. Hera was not fooled by this however, and demanded that Zeus give the heifer to her. She then arranged for Argus with his hundred eyes to watch over Io, and Zeus could do nothing to help her. He finally went to his son Hermes, the messenger of the gods, and asked him to find a way to kill Argus. Hermes disguised himself as a shepherd, and approaching Argus began to chat and play his pipes, hoping to lull the watchman to sleep. To begin with some of the eyes closed while others stayed awake, but finally the story of Pan and Syrinx had the desired effect, all the eyes fell asleep and Hermes was able to kill Argus. It seemed that Io was free then but Hera turned on her again and sent a gad fly to chase and sting her; then Hera took the hundred eyes of Argus and set them in the tail of her favourite bird, the peacock.

Varro (116 – 27 BC) mentions that the Romans "did not blush to give 50 denarii for a young fatted peacock". They also considered peahens' eggs to be a delicacy, a fashion that was started by the orator Quintus Hortensius. Pliny, writing during the next century, tells us that: "Marcus Aufidius Livio was the first to contrive a sure way to fatten peacocks; and he succeeded so well that he made prodigious sums every year by the sale of those birds." The Emperor Vitellius came to power at that time and would make tributes to the goddess Minerva of pike livers, pheasant brains, peacock brains, flamingo tongues and lamprey roes. Extraordinary dishes like these had come into vogue to try to tempt the appetites of rich Romans. Although they did not know it, most of them were suffering from lead poisoning as a result of using lead vessels for cooking and lead pipes for their water supply. Loss of appetite is one of the symptoms of lead poisoning, and this gave rise to the consumption of all kinds of animals, birds and fish which would not normally have been eaten.

St. Augustine of Hippo (354 AD – 430 AD) commented on an alleged strange characteristic of peacock meat in his book "The City of God": "Who but God the creator of all things gave to peacock's flesh the faculty of not putrefying: which thing at first hearing seeming to me incredible. It happened that at Carthage there was set before us a roasted Peacock: which being produced after so many days space as any other roasted flesh would corrupt in, did not at all offend our Nose. Being laid up again, after more than thirty days it was

A 5th century floor mosaic from the church of Multiplication of the Loaves and Fishes, Tabgha, Palestine

found the same as before, and likewise the same after a year, save that it was somewhat drier and a little contracted or shrunk".

Marco Polo who wrote about his travels in the 13th and 14th centuries, tells the story of St. Thomas and the peacock: "We should like to tell you how the saint met his death, as it is reported by the people of the parts. The truth is that Messer St. Thomas was outside his hermitage in the wood, praying to the Lord his God. And round him were many peacocks, for you must know that they are more plentiful here than anywhere in the world. And while he was thus saying his prayers, an idolater of the race and lineage of the gavi, let fly an arrow from his bow, intending to kill one of these peacocks who were round the saint. And he never saw the saint himself. But the shot intended for the peacock hit the saint on the right side. And when he had received the blow he worshipped his creator most fervently, and of that blow he died." This was Doubting Thomas or Didymus, who arrived in India in 52 AD and died in 72 AD.

Marco Polo raised another interesting point when he visited Quilon (Kollam in Kerala): "Then there are peacocks of another sort than ours and much bigger

The altar in the Basilica of St. Thomas, Mylapore near Chennai, India

and handsomer, and the hens too that are unlike ours." Could these have been Javas, or Greens, that had been introduced into India?

In 15th century France Maitre Chiquart, (1420) a renowned chef of that time, prided himself on his ingenuity when preparing peacock: "for an entremets he skins a peacock in the usual way but then substitutes a cooked goose for the peacock's carcass, redressing the goose in the peacock's skin and feathers. The trick, or what he himself calls a pleasant subterfuge, will not be discovered until the diners, expecting to find the normally insipid, tough flesh of the peacock, with delight bite rather into the tender, luscious roast goose".

As time went by gluttony became widespread amongst the wealthy of Europe. In 16th century France Sumptuary Laws (designed to regulate expenditure on luxuries) were imposed in an effort to restrain the French passion for food, while in Venice, pheasant, guineafowl, woodcock and peacock were all banned from menus. Peacock meat was actually considered to have a number of rather serious drawbacks at this time. It was difficult to digest, provided little nourishment, increased black bile and was harmful to those with liver and spleen problems.

In 16th century Spain the peacock had a stately dance named after it. The Spanish word for peacock is 'pavon' and the dance was the pavane where the gentlemen in their long robes of office and the ladies in their trailing gowns

A 12th century frieze of a peacock in the Basilica Museum, Mylapore, India

stalked their partners in the same manner as these beautiful birds.

By the time Alfred Russel Wallace was writing his book "The Malay Archipelago" in 1869, the Green or Java peacock had been discovered. Here is an extract from the book: "Gunong Prau, Wonosalem, is situated about a thousand feet above the sea, but unfortunately it is at a distance from the forest and is surrounded by coffee plantations, thickets of bamboo, and coarse grasses. . . . The place was, however, famous for peacocks, and my boy soon shot several of these magnificent birds, whose flesh we found to be tender, white and delicate, and similar to that of a turkey. The Java peacock is a different species from that in India, the neck being covered with scale-like green feathers, and the crest of a different form; but the

Mosaic showing Noah and the Ark, Basilica of St. Mark, Venice

eyed train is equally large and equally beautiful. It is a singular fact in geographical distribution that the peacock should not be found in Sumatra or Borneo, while the superb Argus, Fired-back and Ocellated pheasants of those islands are equally unknown in Java. Exactly parallel is the fact that in Ceylon and southern India, where the peacock abounds, there are none of the splendid Lophophori and other gorgeous pheasants which inhabit northern India. It would seem as if the peacock can admit of no rivals in its domain."

Mosaic from the floor of the Basilica of St. Mark in Venice

13

Chapter 2
Peacocks and Indian Mythology

As with other animals found in India such as the elephant, the monkey and the lion, so the peacock is bound up with the mythology of Hinduism. Although it may not have a central role, it is often depicted in paintings under trees or in the background.

The word for peacock in Sanskrit is 'mayura' which means killer of killers i.e. snakes, and in India there are many carved images of peacocks with snakes grasped in their feet. In the north of India the word for peacock is 'mor' and in the south 'mayil' with many variations in between.

Vishnu, who has 108 names, always wore a peacock feather in his headband which made him instantly recognisable as the boy Krishna in his 8th incarnation, while Saraswati, the goddess of wisdom and Brahma's wife, is usually depicted with a peacock beside her which was also her sacred mount.

Kartikeya riding on a peacock

Shiva or Siva, the god of creation and destruction, had two sons, the younger of whom was the elephant headed god Ganesh. His elder brother, who is not so well known, was called Kartikeya or Skanda. He was the god of war and is always shown riding on a peacock, his own particular 'vehicle'.

In south east India in the suburbs of Chennai (the new name for Madras) there is a place called Mylapore, 'myla' being Tamil for peacock and 'pore' meaning place or town. Here there is a temple called

Part of the temple of Kapaleeswarar, Mylapore, India

Kapaleeswarar, 'kapale' meaning skull and 'shwara' meaning man. The temple dates back to the 16th century and has a huge multi-carved entrance building or gopuram some 40 metres or 130 feet high. This temple to Shiva contains the story of how the goddess Uma, better known as Parvati, wanted to marry Shiva. She made a penance which involved being transformed into a peacock, and Shiva accepted her hand in marriage. She then reverted to her human form and they were married under a punnai tree. One of these trees is growing in the temple courtyard and has now become a wishing tree with dozens of ribbons, strips of cloth and messages tied to its branches. Peacock effigies abound in and around the temple and entry is free although non-believers are only allowed as far as the courtyard.

There are many Indian legends concerning peacocks. It is said that they frequent old houses and trees because their presence will return them to their former glories; these birds know they are beautiful but when they look at their feet they start to weep. Being naturally shy they have only rarely been seen mating in the wild; Indian folklore suggests that the male bird drops a jewel from his beak and the female picks it up and is fertilized. Because the peacock is known to kill snakes there is a belief that its bile and blood act as an antidote to snake poison and that smoke from burnt peacock feathers helps to dispel the venom. Other parts of the bird's body are said to cure many diseases from asthma, headaches, catarrh and paralysis, to infertility and tuberculosis.

Chapter 3
Good and Bad Luck

For some strange reason peacocks have always been associated with either good or bad luck. In India they are revered and if you are lucky enough to witness the peacock dance during one of their courtship rituals, you will be fortunate indeed. The blue of the peacock's neck is a lucky colour. When Indian students are studying for their exams they like to use a peacock's feather as a book mark to bring them luck, and in former times Indian poets would use peacocks' feathers to write love poems with.

In this country however, it has always been a very different story. Here are some extracts from "The Peacock's Pleasaunce" by "E.V.B." that was published nearly a century ago:

"And there is the monastic legend that makes the Peacock unblest for young children. The story of how the Holy Family in their flight from Egypt, sheltered in the centre of a thick juniper tree – Herod's horsemen being close at their heels. It was a wild place, and the gorse pods all around kept crackling and bursting open, and peacocks screamed and disturbed the child, who began to cry and was nearly discovered by the soldiers. So Mary rose up and banned them all round! . . . And that is why gorse is never permitted in gardens, and why peacocks are unlucky to babies. . . ."

"There is an oft-told story of a country house and a lady who one day while sitting in the drawing room upstairs, laughing and talking with a party of friends, suddenly exclaimed, – starting up and hurrying to the window, – "Oh, the Peacock!" She opened the window and instantly disappeared. The startled guests who had rushed after her, looking down beheld the lady lying dead upon the gravel beneath the window, whilst a beautiful peacock stood near her in his Pride, with his round of outspread plumes."

"Another tale is told of a fine old mansion somewhere in Wales that had remained empty and tenantless for a number of years. A tenant at last was found; and the family arrived on a brilliant day in the middle of June. It is said they all went out into the garden, and round to the stable court-yard to meet the horses coming from town. They heard their tramp and the voices of the stablemen who were bringing them in, and one of the ladies went forward before the others to receive and welcome her own favourite riding horse, a beautiful grey, whom she saw just entering through the gate, led by the stud-groom. The horse advanced with a little neigh of recognition, but had no sooner stepped into the court-yard than he suddenly stopped short, reared up, and the next moment fell back dead at his mistress' feet.

A few days after the owner of the house received a letter from his new tenant, stating that an over-mantel above the fire-place in one of the principal rooms in the house had been the cause of the death of a valuable horse, and praying that it might be at once removed out of the house lest a worse thing should happen. This over-mantle had a certain value of its own. It was a kind of drapery or hanging, made of peacocks' feathers, enwound with blue and green, and wrought curiously in gold thread and silken needlework, and sparkling with gems. It had been the gift of a dear friend, and had been sent from the Indies – long ago. It was removed and buried with the horse, and thereafter those tenants slept in peace."

Peacock Decorations

If you are in Europe and are interested to see peacock decorations then you should go to visit the Linderhof Castle near Munich in Germany where there is a beautiful collection of peacock artefacts. The castle was built by King Ludwig the second between 1870 and 1878 in the Rococo style. The king's two favourite birds were peacocks and swans. In the West Gobelin Room stands a life size painted porcelain peacock from Sevres (France); another stands in the East Gobelin Room. The rooms were the creation of the Paris Gobelin factory. In the grounds there is a Moorish kiosk with an exotic interior: in the curve of the apse stands a peacock throne created for the king in 1877 by Le Blanc-Granger in Paris. There is also a silk covered divan which is crowned on the arms and backrest by three colourful enamelled wrought iron peacocks whose trains are formed from Polish Bohemian glass.

The Minton peacock in the photograph was recently sold at Bonhams, the London auctioneers and valuers. There is a copy in the Flagstaff Hill Museum, Wamambool, Australia.

A life size Majolica figure of a peacock, 1873.

17

Chapter 4
Observations

This is a collection of observations on peafowl which you might find interesting.

The name derives from medieval English, pe or pea-cock. It had many different forms in those days, for example: pecok, pyckock, poucock, pocok, poocock and pacock. The Latin for peacock is Pavo and from this root we have pavone in Italian, pavon in Spanish, paon in French and pfau in German.

Peacocks' train feathers are some of the longest in the bird world. Both peacocks and peahens display although the hens only do so occasionally. Most people think that the train feathers are the tail feathers but this is not the case. Gilbert White writing in 1771 in his book "The Natural History of Selbourne", puts this very succinctly: "Happening to make a visit to my neighbour's peacocks, I could not help observing that the trains of these magnificent birds appear by no means to be their tails; those long feathers growing not from their uropigium but all up their backs. A range of short brown stiff feathers, about six inches long, fixed in the uropigium is the real tail, and serves as a fulcrum to prop up the train, which is long and top-heavy, when set on end. When the train is up, nothing appears of the bird before but its head and neck; but this would not be the case were those long feathers fixed only in the rump, as may be seen by the turkey cock, when in strutting attitude. By a strong muscular vibration these birds can make the shafts of their long feathers clatter like swords of a sword dancer; they then trample very quick with their feet, and run backwards towards the females." To raise his train feathers the male first shakes them out sideways parallel with the ground,

Green male, front

Green male, back

then they are pushed up into a vertical position by the true tail feathers. By tilting his body forward he can make the train feathers cup forwards as though to focus on the hen, while periodically rustling and rattling the feathers with a twitch of his abdominal muscles.

When a male displays it is usually a trigger to any others in the vicinity to start displaying as well. The females are attracted to the males that have the longest trains with the most 'eyes'. Some trains reach to 1.5m or 5ft in length. Strangely, white females are more attracted to blue males than white ones.

When they live in the wild, peacocks share a communal displaying area or 'lek' where they parade round hoping to attract females. The young cock birds display too on the edges of the 'lek' hoping for a chance. There is rarely any fighting in these natural conditions as the males seem to realize instinctively that the longer and more intact their train feathers are, the more chances they have of winning females; fighting would be counter productive. As the male matures, his train feathers grow, so a female knows that a long train belongs to a mature male who has been successful in combating both predators and disease.

Peacocks prefer to display when it is cool, not in the blazing sun. They are also vulnerable to attack when displaying which is one reason why they wheel about, not only to focus on the female, but also to keep an eye on what is going on around them. The female often carries on pecking about completely unimpressed, taking no notice at all of the cock bird's display which can last up to 45 minutes.

Like most prey species, peafowl have all-round vision. They prefer to use their long legs to run if they are pursued and can jump up to 2m or 6ft high. When alarmed by a ground predator, a group of them will pull themselves up as tall as they can, ruffle their neck feathers like bottle brushes and give their alarm call, often surrounding the rat, weasel or snake etc. until it has run off in fright. They are never too far from water in the wild but they will not actually bathe in it, preferring to take dust baths instead.

Male birds are best kept singly as two or more do tend to set each other off with their calls. They can also be very stupid with anything shiny or reflective such as a car door or French window, seeing a reflection and trying to attack it; they will peck and stab, often injuring themselves and leaving a bloody mess. They can become very tame but some of them are also extremely demanding and aggressive with food so do be aware of this if you are open to the public and/or have friends over for a picnic in the garden. Normally the tamer the birds the less fertile they are. Peacocks can live for 20 years or more. A gathering or flock of peafowl is called a muster.

Chapter 5
Wild Peacocks in India

In early January 2003 we flew to India to look at peacocks in the wild. The peacock is India's national bird. It is found in most states and is common in Madhya Pradesh, Rajasthan and the Punjab. I had been to India before in 1965 when I drove round the country in a Landrover. In those days kerbstones were just being laid along the edges of the pavements in New Delhi and people were grumbling about the innovation, but now the capital is fast catching up with the West.

Our 12 day trip was to take us south and west of New Delhi into the state of Madhya Pradesh and then across to Rajasthan. South of Agra is a town and district called Morena, 'mor' being the Hindi word for peacock, where these birds abound in the fields. The area around Morena is ideal for peafowl as it is dotted with patches of woodland in which they roost at night, and the farmland is well mechanised and mostly irrigated. Water is vital for peacocks and there is a plentiful supply for irrigation coming from the mighty Chambal. This river is home to fresh water dolphins, huge fish-eating crocodiles called gharials and river crocodiles which are locally known as muggars or magars. I wonder if our word 'mug' (attack) might have originated from this name. . . .

The peafowl can be seen feeding in the stubble fields and picking their way in and out of crops such as wheat, barley, pearl millet and mustard. They look rather like large pheasants from a distance and are shy when approached. The

A group of wild Indian Blue peafowl in a field of mustard stubble, Morena, India

The Peacock Gate in the City Palace, Jaipur, Rajasthan, India

Detail from the Peacock Gate

farmers tolerate them, as peacocks have a place in the Hindu religion. They eat the seeds from weeds and crops and help to keep snakes down as well: another Indian word for peacock is mayura which means killer of killers i.e. snakes.

We came to Morena not only to see peacocks but to try to find out why they are dying in certain areas. The locals seemed to believe that there was a gang of 'bad people' who had poisoned large numbers of them with agricultural chemicals. This had alarmed the authorities who thought these birds were dying from pesticide residues in the crops. Pesticides, particularly DDT, are a problem in certain parts of India and most drinking water contains far more than the permitted levels of residues. It is thought that this is what has caused a drastic decline in the vulture population. When I visited India in 1965 we were able to see the clearings on the outskirts of villages where people disposed of dead animals; anything that had died, cows, pigs or dogs, was dragged there and left for the vultures to pick over. You could get quite close to them as they were often too sated with food to fly off, but they are rarely seen now except in the wild life reserves. I was reliably informed that the vultures which used to perform this vital service, would pick up and eat dead egrets from the fields which had themselves ingested poisoned frogs and insects and died from chemical poisoning as a result.

Wild Indian Blue male, Ranthambore National Park, Rajasthan, India

Our travels took us next to Rajasthan. Here we drove round three national parks, Shivpuri, Ranthambore and Sariska, as well as passing through several farming areas where peacocks thrived. Of the three parks Ranthambore is the best known and the best looked after, despite not having seen any rain for the past two years. Because of the drought there was a watering scheme in operation. As the lakes and rivers dried up, holes were dug and tankers came each day to fill them, so most of the animals and birds were never too far from a watering hole.

It was interesting to note that of all the wild peafowl we came across, there was no diversity in colour and we saw no white birds. I believe that white peacocks do exist in India but it was suggested that these had been imported. Some of the males did appear to have more iridescent blue necks than others but that may have been the effect of the light at the time or the stage of feather growth.

Wild Indian Blue females, Ranthambore National Park, Rajasthan, India

As it was January the males' trains were not fully grown, as can be seen in the photographs. On the whole these wild peacocks appeared slightly smaller than the domesticated birds we are familiar with, and rather longer in the leg.

All the parks had populations of tigers, but seeing these elusive and mainly nocturnal animals was very much a matter of chance. We came close several times and all the wildlife in the vicinity set up a fearful clamour: the peacocks shrieked and stretched their necks straight up in the air like periscopes to peer over the grasses, monkeys howled and deer barked. The atmosphere was electric and very tense. Sadly all we saw of a tiger was a large paw mark in the dust but that was a lot better than nothing!

On a few occasions we were able to see just how strong peacocks are in flight, particularly at roosting time; they were always some of the last birds to settle for the night. At Ranthambore there was an old fort on top of the hill which dominated the park. Peacocks regularly soared perhaps 150 feet to the tops of the walls in the evening, while down below in the villages we were able to watch their big black silhouettes flying up to settle in the shade trees at dusk. Things were not easy for the farmers in that area. They had to bring in all their livestock at night to protect them from tigers and leopards, and they guarded their fields during the hours of darkness as well. This was because there was such a serious shortage of vegetation owing to the drought that the deer, antelopes and gazelles from the park were coming down after dark and helping themselves to the farmers' crops. Each night men would camp out in little huts dotted round the fields and we would hear distant shouts and bangs as they kept up a constant barrage of noise to frighten off any marauders. Because the livestock were corralled at night the leopards and tigers usually only took dogs we were told.

By March or April male peacocks have grown their trains, and their shrill cries in June and July herald the coming of the rainy season. It is during this period that they put on their courtship displays. The females lay their eggs on the ground, usually 7 to 10 in a clutch, in August and September. Although they hide their nests in the lush grass, the sitting birds and eggs are always vulnerable to predation from mongooses, jackals, leopards and tigers. The chick survival rate is 3 to 5 per brood depending on the season. Once they are up and about the threat from hawks, buzzards and eagles increases considerably.

Despite Hindu beliefs there is evidence that peacocks are being killed not only for their body parts which are being sold abroad, but also to be eaten at so called smart business and VIP functions. There has been a call to ban the trade in peacock feathers. These are frequently seen made up into fans which are said to ward off evil spirits. Hawkers sell them at all the popular tourist sites.

On our trip we saw only a very small part of what is an enormous and fascinating country. The different regions were wonderfully varied and the people we met were always most friendly and polite. If you ever have the opportunity to go, don't hesitate.

Chapter 6
Types of Peafowl

Peafowl belong to the pheasant family. They consist of three main groups: Pavo christatus (Indian or blue peafowl), Pavo muticus (Green peafowl) and Afropavo congensis (Congo or African peafowl).

Pavo christatus, Indian or Blue peafowl

This is the bird that most people are familiar with. It has a dazzling blue neck, iridescent green feathers bordered with black on its back and buff feathers mottled or barred with black on its shoulders. The crest on its head consists of a bunch of about 25 'stalks' topped with tiny blue fans, and its magnificent eyed train can be as much as five feet long. The hen is rather drab in comparison with a greyish brown body and bronzy green neck. This colouring works well as camouflage when she is sitting on her eggs.

Distribution: blue peafowl are found in most parts of India and Sri Lanka, eastern Pakistan and the foothills of the Himalayas. They are very common in certain Indian states such as the Punjab, Rajasthan and Madhya Pradesh.

Indian Blue female

Indian Blue male

Pavo muticus, Green peafowl

This species is not as common as the Indian peafowl and has some striking differences. It is larger with more white in the face and its crest consists of a long tuft of erect metallic green feathers; its eyed train is greener than that of the Indian peafowl. Its body is covered with scale-like greeny blue and bronze feathers and the female looks very similar. Green peafowl have longer legs than Indian peafowl and their call is a hoot rather than a shriek. There are three sub species:

Pavo muticus muticus
The Java green peafowl. This is the greenest of all the three sub species. Distribution: Java, Indonesia.

Pavo muticus imperator, the Indo-Chinese green peafowl
This bird is a more bronzy green than the Java peafowl. Distribution: the Malay peninsular, parts of Thailand, Cambodia, Vietnam, Laos and southern China.

Indo-Chinese Green or Imperator male

Indo-Chinese Green or Imperator female

Pavo muticus spicifer, the Burmese green peafowl
This species is a duller green bordering on blue. Distribution: north east India and Burma.

These three sub species ideally need to be seen together for their subtle differences to be appreciated. There is a potential problem with a few captive breeding programmes, as in some cases the various Greens are being interbred and their differences are becoming less noticeable.

Afropavo congensis, Congo or African peafowl

This is the smallest of the peafowl family with the birds no bigger than chickens; in some ways they resemble certain pheasants, especially during their courtship displays. Both sexes have erect bristly hair/feather crests, the males' black and white, the females' more reddish brown. The male's lower neck and breast is a deep violet, the female's is brown. Both sexes have bronzy green backs, lighter and more metallic in the female. The tails of both are much shorter than those of the Asiatic species, being only 8 or 9 inches long (20 to 23 cms). The tail of the cock bird has no ocelli or eye feathers and is far more akin to a turkey's tail than the train of the Asiatic species.

Distribution: the African peafowl is found in east central Congo (formerly the Belgian Congo) now called Zaire. It is a very shy bird and was only discovered in 1936. It is not possible to say how many of these birds are living in the wild due to their remote jungle habitat, political problems in the country and the fact that they are so shy, but there are approximately 150 in captivity world-wide. They are officially listed as 'vulnerable' but there are captive breeding programmes taking place in America as well as at London Zoo, Chester Zoo and Jersey Zoo with Antwerp Zoo, Belgium, in control. African peafowl can be seen at all these zoos.

Congo peafowl

Chapter 7
Colour Mutations

There are three species of peafowl, two of which are used for crossing to make colour mutations. The third which is the African peafowl is so rare that it is enough just to breed these in captivity.

Colour mutations do not occur in the wild mainly due to the wide genetic diversity in their habitat, and being a prey species, white or pied peafowl would not normally last long in the wild. This is why one very rarely sees anything except blue peafowl in India.

Colour mutations are created in captive breeding programmes where birds are closely bred, father to daughter, mother to son, brother to sister etc. There are tried and tested rules of inbreeding as set out by Gregor Mendel, A.L. Hagedoorn, R. Punnett and others. I suspect that most colour combinations of peafowl were randomly selected and put together to 'see what came out', although I do understand that poultry genetic technology was applied at the time. One of the consequences of this form of inbreeding is a high failure rate, infertile eggs, embryos dead in shell, deformities and single sex chicks.

It is certainly a challenge trying to produce an ever more beautiful peacock, the main difficulty being trying to ensure the same mutation in both sexes. When you think of the colour and size variations in hens, rabbits or pigeons for instance, you can begin to understand why people are so fascinated with this area of breeding.

Mutations started to be recorded in the 1800s, first the Black Shoulder, a mutation of the Indian Blue, then the White and the Pied. (The White is not an albino as the iris of the eye is blue.) It was not until the mid 1900s that new colour mutations and hybrids started to appear, the result of crossing Blues with Whites, Pieds, Black Shoulders and Greens. The Spaulding is a cross between the Green and the Blue named after a Mrs. Spaulding who created it.

These mutations and crosses are frowned upon by purists who are concerned, particularly as we now have genetic manipulation, that these birds could infiltrate the wild stock. Captive bred birds, looking to all intents and purposes like pure Blues or Greens, are now being sold abroad when they are actually genetically impure. There may well soon be a DNA database for peafowl.

Emerald Spalding

Cameo hen

29

Black Shoulder Purple

Purple hen

Charcoal

Charcoal hen

31

Purple

Opal Black Shoulder

32

Blue Pied

Silver Pied cock

Chapter 8
How to Keep Peacocks

Problems with noise

Before you start to keep these birds it is essential that you are aware of the noise factor. Indian peacocks shriek for about 4 months of the year from April to August after which time the train feathers start to fall out. The birds are normally quite quiet for the rest of the year but can be set off by any sudden loud noises such as shouting, gunfire or car alarms. Their calls carry for a considerable distance. Green peacocks make a different sound, a kind of hooting noise which is less intrusive than that of the Indian peacock. Do remember that these calls are not confined to the daylight hours! Peacocks are not recommended for built up areas, but are better in country properties. Warwick Castle which is on the edge of the town of Warwick near Stratford upon Avon, has had peafowl for years, and I know these birds occasionally stray into the neighbouring streets and gardens. With more and more people buying country properties these days, it is important that everyone is aware of the rules and regulations regarding noise pollution; even the poor village church bells are sometimes under threat! So it is essential to think carefully about this and discuss your plans with your neighbours.

Peafowl in the garden

When you first get your Indian peafowl you will have to confine them in an aviary for about 3 months so they can orientate themselves and get used to their surroundings. You can then let them out and they will just use the aviary to roost in at night unless you have a lot of space and trees that they can use instead. If you have Green peafowl they will have to live permanently in an aviary because they will always wander off if given their freedom.

Pied peacock in Cairo Zoo, Egypt

Peafowl can be very destructive in gardens. They particularly love aromatic plants like lavender or thyme and will stand and stamp on them as if to benefit from the aroma. Some people prefer to keep their peafowl shut in their aviaries during

Black Shouldered male   *Black Shouldered female*

the months of March, April and May, in order to allow spring plants to establish themselves. If the birds are to be let out they do need a large area of lawns and trees.

Location of the aviary

Peacocks must have access to plenty of sun and shade but need to be sheltered from winds and draughts. You can make your aviary into a striking feature in a garden or arboretum, or simply join it onto a garage or stable; it all depends on the lay-out of your property. Be aware of the possible effect of echoes from the peacocks' calls and avoid siting your aviary under deciduous trees: they would cut off the sun in the summer and shed branches, leaves and twigs on the roof in the autumn and winter.

The site should be well drained or provision should be made to ensure that the floor of the aviary is as dry as possible.

Dimensions of the aviary

The larger you can make your aviary the better. The minimum size for a pair of Indian peafowl can be 4m x 4m (12ft x 12ft) by 2m (6ft) high, but for a pair of Green peafowl or a trio of Indian peafowl you really need 8m or 10m x 5m (24ft or 30ft x 15ft) and 2m (6ft) high. These larger aviaries can be higher, up to 3m or 4m (9ft or 12ft) if necessary.

Planning the lay-out of your aviary

The aviary must be south facing and of course needs an access door for cleaning and/or driving the birds in at night. It is sensible to put this at one end so the peacocks can be herded along a wall or fence and in through the door. Bear in mind the position of the shelter or winter accommodation, and if you are planning an adjoining aviary, the location of the door(s) in relation to this shelter is important. When you are moving your birds from one to another, leave the doors open so they can find their own way rather than be driven in.

Shelter or winter accommodation

This will vary from a simple shelter in milder parts of the country to insulated housing in areas where the winters are harsh. A shelter consists of a building with three and a half sides and a sloping roof so rain water runs away from the aviary. This allows the birds to get out of the rain and to perch at night in the dry. The floor must be covered in sand. These shelters are usually without doors.

For winter accommodation a wooden building about 3m x 2.5m (10ft x 8ft) is ideal. It must be raised off the ground about 20cms or 8 or 9 inches to stop rats from burrowing underneath. The floor needs a thick covering of wood shavings to prevent the birds developing Bumblefoot (see section on Diseases page 55) when they jump down from the perch. There should be a door to give access for cleaning, either leading in from outside which is probably more convenient, or opening into the aviary. There must also be a pop hole about .75m x .75m (2ft x 2ft) for the peafowl. This building can be insulated, roof, walls and floor, and internal walls added in areas where there are severe frosts. A glass window (double glazed) and guarded with wire mesh is important to allow daylight into the shed. Some people like to provide a heat lamp inside as well, but this is really only necessary in some northern and central parts of the U.S.A., Canada and Europe.

The floor

As we have already mentioned, the floor of your aviary must be well drained. A muddy floor leads to all sorts of problems: the train feathers become caked in dirt and there is an increased risk of diseases such as Coccidiosis and Gapes. You may have to raise the floor with concrete block work and then backfill with stone and gravel before you finish off with a layer of

A stone peacock bracket in the Raj Mahal, Orchha, India

soil. If you want to put small trees or plants in the aviary you will have to make wells for them to grow in. It's important to provide a sandy pathway around the inside of the perimeter fence about 1m or 1yd wide as the birds do like to patrol their territory (or look for a way out!) If the aviary floor does become muddy, put down a bed of straw as a temporary solution to the problem, and it is a good idea to place paving slabs at access points to prevent soggy patches and erosion.

Perches

These must be round or half round with a diameter of 8cm to 10cm (3" to 4"). If they are any smaller they are uncomfortable to use and can cause deformed breast bones in younger birds. The height should be above 1.2m or 4ft so that the train feathers clear the ground. The birds will naturally go to roost on the highest perch which should be in the shelter area. There should also be at least one perch in the aviary as the peafowl do use them during the day. If you have Green peafowl remove the perches in the outside part of their aviary during the winter so that they can only perch inside and then they will avoid any frosts there might be. Make sure there is enough perching room and allow about 30cm to 40cm (12" to 16") per bird.

A droppings board under the main roost perch is recommended as this helps to ensure the general cleanliness of the aviary; peafowl manure tends to be runny and very messy.

White peafowl in a barn

Water

Peafowl drink a lot hence the runny droppings. Use any large container for their water but make sure it is easy to clean out. Raise it off the ground to stop leaves or soil from being blown or kicked into it, and make sure it is in the shade so green algae doesn't have a chance to form in the sun. You must provide your peafowl with fresh water every day.

Planting

Peacocks are not sympathetic gardeners so whatever you plant in the aviary must be robust. Slow growing conifers are good as they come in a range of colours and are unpalatable. To begin with their root systems will have to be protected with stones or wire mesh pegged to the ground. Beware of spiky plants which could shred your peacocks' train feathers.

Dust Bath

This must be under cover to keep the contents dry and can be in a separate place or built into the shelter area. Use a mixture of sand and sieved wood ash together with a sprinkling of poultry anti-louse and flea powder.

Construction

An aviary can be made of iron or wood; both materials have their advantages and the choice is up to the individual. I personally find metal rather cold but it does last longer with the correct painting or treatment, and you can achieve designs that are not possible in wood, and have much slimmer supports. On the other hand treated wood looks more natural, has a life span of 20 years or more depending on its location and is easier to work. (Always remember to paint cut ends with treatment solution.) Whatever you decide on, it's important that your aviary blends in with its surroundings.

Most people today use weld-mesh instead of wire-mesh because it is stronger and more rigid, but it is more expensive. Some people mistakenly think that a small mesh at the bottom will keep rats out, but rats, like their bushy tailed cousins, can climb to great heights. Use a 5cm x 5cm (2" x 2") mesh and if you don't like the colour you can paint it with a bitumen paint and roller.

When constructing your aviary roof make sure it is strongly supported otherwise the weight of frozen snow in winter might well bring it down. Don't use Netlon or plastic netting on the roof or sides as squirrels will eat holes in it and it degrades in the sunlight.

Some people prefer to keep their peafowl on a 'verandah'. This is a large aviary with a raised wire floor made from 1.5cm (.5") weld mesh. There are several advantages in this system. First of all there are no problems with Blackhead or Coccidiosis and secondly the vermin problem is reduced. Having said this, neither of these diseases is usually a problem, but in certain parts of the world the risk may be greater. A large nest box with pop holes is attached to the raised aviary

Decorative peacocks, Jahangir Mahal, Orchha, India

affording the peahens seclusion and privacy in which to lay their eggs. Put in some straw or other suitable nesting material.

Tidying up

One of the joys of keeping birds in an aviary is being able to show them to your friends; they certainly won't want to be met with the sight of an untidy enclosure littered with fallen leaves and old feathers. It is surprising the amount of debris that can accumulate, particularly in late summer. Whether you have a large property open to the public or a small aviary in your back garden, it is always important to keep things clean and tidy, so a quick run round with a spring tined rake daily or as regularly as possible, keeps the pen looking smart. Droppings should be removed from under the night perch and fresh sand or shavings introduced.

A stylized peacock painting circa 1530, Orchha, India

Where can I buy peafowl?

It is best to buy your birds from a reputable source. There is an organisation in America called the United Peafowl Association which has members in most states who should be able to help, and in England there is the World Pheasant Association which also has members across the country including Quinton Spratt, who is Europe's largest peafowl breeder.

Chapter 9
General Management and Breeding

It is important to plan the layout of your aviaries with care. If access is easy then the job of keeping the aviary and accommodation clean should be simple. Each day top up your birds' food hopper or feeder and clean and refill the water bowl. Don't forget to clean out the food hopper every now and then as it will get clogged with dust and worse, mouldy food and debris at the bottom. Look at your birds and check that they respond to you by offering some bread or a few sultanas or shelled peanuts.

Don't forget to prune the foliage in the aviary from time to time and replace any plants if necessary.

At weekends perhaps, or when you have a little more time try making a special dish for your peafowl to add some variety to their diet. (See section on Food, page 53.)

If your birds are free range they still need feeding of course and must have access to fresh water at all times.

A head count is a good idea especially during the breeding season, and don't forget to worm your birds. (See section on Diseases, page 55).

How to Catch Peafowl

There are two main ways to catch a peafowl, one is to drive it into a building and corner it, the other is to use a fisherman's landing net. Always grab the bird's legs when catching it and avoid the feathers as they pull out very easily. If you use a net it must be at least 45 to 50cms wide (18 to 20 inches). Drop it over the head, neck and front end of the body then grab the bird's legs to extricate it from the net.

To hold it, grasp the bird firmly round both legs and either let its breast rest on top of your other arm or tuck the front half of its body under that arm and gently squeeze it to you.

Most peafowl are transported as young birds in plastic crates; adult birds can be put in large cardboard boxes on a bed of shavings with ventilation holes cut into the sides. There is no need to provide food and water for short journeys.

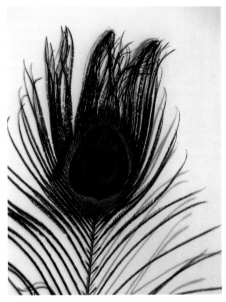

Sayings

Gilbert White, "The Natural History of Selbourne" 1771:
"And first the peacock with its gorgeous train, demands our attention; but like most of the gaudy birds, his notes are grating and shocking to the ear. The yelling of cats and braying of an ass are not more disgustful."

John Ruskin, 1819 – 1900:
"Remember that the most beautiful things in the world are the most useless; peacocks and lilies for instance."

John Ruskin, 1819 – 1900:
"I do not believe that any peacock envies another peacock his tail, because every peacock is persuaded that his own tail is the finest in the world. The consequence of this is that peacocks are peaceable birds."

Oscar Wilde, 1854 – 1900:
"She is a peacock in everything but beauty."

The Italians say: "the feathers of an angel, the voice of a devil and the appetite of a thief."

At twenty a man is a peacock, at thirty a lion, at forty a camel, at fifty a serpent, at sixty a dog, at seventy an ape, at eighty nothing at all.

Chapter 10
Incubation, Hatching and Rearing

Collect the peahens' eggs daily and wash them in a proprietary egg washing solution mixed with warm water. When they are dry store them on their sides either on sand or in egg trays. Turn the eggs once a day, first clockwise and the next day anti-clockwise. This is to prevent the yolk from getting stuck to the membrane inside the egg. If you keep turning the eggs in the same direction the chalazae or strings that hold the yolk in position, will get twisted. To help you remember which way to turn the eggs, mark an 'x' on one side of the shell with a pencil and an 'o' on the other side. For optimum hatching results don't store the eggs for longer than 10 days. The incubation temperature is 37.5 degrees C and incubation time is 26 days.

The fertility of the Blue peafowl is usually 70% and the Green is 60%. Early eggs are more fertile than late eggs. Pure bred peachicks of both colours look identical as day olds.

There are three ways to hatch peafowl eggs: A) in an incubator, B) under a broody hen or bantam, C) under a peahen.

Peahen eggs, reading from top left clockwise, Green, Blue, Black Shouldered, White. These colours will vary slightly from bird to bird and breed to breed.

A) Hatching in an incubator

For a detailed account of incubation see our book in the Gold Cockerel Series "Incubation at Home". Meanwhile here is a brief synopsis of the procedure.

There are many types of incubator on the market; some turn the eggs automatically, some you have to rock to turn the eggs and others you turn manually. The automatic machines turn about 9 times in 24 hours but if you are doing it manually, 3 times a day is fine. Always turn an odd number of times each day then the eggs will not be left lying on one side for too long.

Make sure that your incubator has been thoroughly disinfected with a proper sterilizing agent, and then let it run for a few days at the correct temperature.

An incubator (Western)   *Packing eggs into incubator trays*

Put in the eggs and allow a little while for the temperature to come back to 37.5 degrees C.

It is vital to have the correct level of humidity in your incubator. As a general rule you put in half a cup of water when you load the machine and then nothing more until the day before the eggs are due to hatch, when you fill up the water containers. But a lot depends on where the incubator is situated, how damp or dry the surroundings are, what altitude you live at, and the weather conditions at the time of incubation.

Candle the eggs at 10 days. This is a way of checking the development of the embryo by shining a strong light through the egg shell, and you can do it using a proper candling box or a powerful torch in a darkened room. Any clear (infertile) eggs or embryos that have stopped developing can be removed. Candle again at day 20 and remove any more dud eggs if necessary then wait for the hatching.

When the chicks hatch leave them to dry out in the incubator. They don't need any food for a while as they absorb the yolk of the egg and live off that for the first 24 to 48 hours.

Hatching time

B) Hatching under a broody hen

Having decided to use a broody, first get her settled into a coop or broody box by moving her at night and putting her on dummy eggs. Check her the next morning, taking her off the nest to feed, drink and empty herself. Before putting her back dust her with

Broodies sitting tight on peafowl eggs

flea/louse powder, as a broody with fleas will not stay the course but keep getting up as she is irritated by these insects. After she has sat on her dummy eggs for a few days, put the peafowl eggs under her, removing the dummies as you do so. A hen will normally cope with 5 peahen eggs and a bantam with 4. Don't forget to check your broody every day and make sure she feeds, drinks and empties herself. All this is described in detail in our book "Chickens at Home" in the Gold Cockerel Series.

At day 10 candle the eggs and take out any infertile ones or eggs in which the embryo has stopped growing, then do the same again on day 20. See also the section on Hatching in an Incubator (page 43).

When the broody has hatched all her eggs move her and the chicks to a coop and run. They will need a drinker with water and some pheasant or turkey starter crumbs. The hen will look after her chicks from now on and if your circumstances allow, will enjoy being let out into the garden with them. Don't forget to shut them up at night though!

As the poults grow so their food requirements will change from pheasant or turkey starter crumbs, to mini pellets, to pheasant or turkey grower pellets. (See chapter 12 Food, page 53.)

One problem when rearing peafowl chicks with a broody hen is that they become imprinted on her, that is, their instincts tell them that she is their mother and they will follow her everywhere. Many a time I have seen peafowl crammed into hen houses or perched above their old 'mum' in a barn or stable. You can break this imprinting if you wean the young adults away from the broody by putting them into a separate pen away from her.

C) Hatching under a peahen

This quite often comes about more by accident than design when the peahen goes off to nest by herself and then reappears with 8 or so chicks. Peahens are attentive mothers so if you have space you can let them out into the garden to forage about, but they should be driven into a stable, shed or aviary at night to protect them from foxes or other predators. You will notice that the young begin to fly quite well at 10 to 15 days old and may want to roost with their mother in some low tree. If you provide ladder perches in their night time shelter they will feel more secure. The range of pheasant or turkey rearer food should be offered but a good deal of their intake will come from foraging about.

If space is not available or there is danger from predators then the peahen and chicks should be given an aviary to themselves; keep out any males as they could trample on the young chicks.

Peachicks, left Green, right Indian Blue   *Day old peachicks, left White, right Black Shouldered*

Rearing

If you are using an incubator for your eggs you will need to prepare a rearing area in good time before they hatch. Make a pen using a piece of hardboard 183cms (6ft) x 61cms (2ft) fastened together at the ends with two strong bulldog clips to form a circle You will then need a heat lamp, cardboard litter or dust-extracted white wood shavings, a drinker and a feeder. Set up your rearing area in a quiet, warm room or shed free from cats, dogs, rats, mice or any sudden noises. Put the chicks into the pen under the heat lamp, making sure that they have enough room to get away from the heat if they become too hot. It is best to use a ceramic bulb which produces 'dark heat' and no light so the chicks can sleep more naturally. Also, ceramic bulbs don't shatter if they get wet. Put in the drinker and feeder but keep them away from the lamp as the

heat can affect the vitamins in the food. Feed your chicks pheasant or turkey starter crumbs.

After a week the chicks should be allowed access to short grass and sunshine. This is particularly important for Green peafowl chicks as they must have sunshine to thrive. Make a run about 3m x 183cms (10ft

Four day old Green peachicks

x 6ft) and cover the top and some of the sides with plastic sheet netting to protect them from wind and rain. Fix some netting across the top and cover half with plastic to ensure a dry area in the pen.

When your chicks are 4 weeks old you can introduce some mini-pellets into their diet. Unlike turkey chicks young peafowl are not shy feeders. You may have to wing-clip them at this stage to prevent them from flying up and banging their heads on the roof of the pen.

At 10 to 12 weeks you can start feeding pheasant or turkey grower pellets to your poults. At this stage they will need more living space: the rearing pen should be at least 15m x 15m (15yds x 15yds) and 2m or 6ft high with a soft Netlon ceiling of 5cm x 5cm (2" x 2") mesh, no smaller or the birds could hang themselves if they fly up in a panic. This area should accommodate one to two dozen birds.

Mixed group of peafowl chicks under a lamp. Note the cardboard chippings.

As they grow into young adults they can be moved into a holding pen with shelter and perches so they can be sorted out for selling or kept for breeding. They should now be eating pheasant or turkey maintenance pellets together with mixed corn and mixed grit. Make sure there is always plenty of fresh water available for your birds.

Young Green peafowl enjoying a grassy run.

Young Green peafowl in a large covered run.

Chapter 11
Breeding

Blue and Green peafowl normally start to breed in their third year but some early hatched Blues will start in their second year.

There are two main ways to breed peafowl, free range or in aviaries.

Breeding free range

If you have a number of birds and a suitable area such as an orchard or walled garden you can breed free range providing you take certain precautions: the area must be fenced and netted across the top or it must be fenced or walled to a height of 2.5m (8ft) and the birds must be wing clipped. In the latter situation where there is no netting over the top of the enclosure you must make sure that there are no handy take-off points like buildings or trees, shrubs or gates near the perimeter fence. Peafowl can jump up to 1.8m (6ft) and will use lower objects from which to jump over the fence.

You must provide adequate shelter, roosting space and shade in your free range area, and create some nesting sites round tree trunks or shrubs using branches of fir or Cupressus.

It must be said that this method of breeding is the most natural and probably best for the birds. The cocks can establish a stamping ground or lek, and the hens can

| *Indian Blue chick* | *Indian Blue chick with female* |

choose their own nesting sites, though a few hens may all choose to nest in the same place.

Make sure you provide several food hoppers and drinkers just in case there is any bullying. Don't forget that when the birds have moulted in late summer they will start to regrow their flight feathers so you will have to clip their wings again.

Wing clipping

To a certain extent this free range method will work if you have a trio of Blues or Black Shoulders or Whites in an aviary and you let them out during the day. Peahens will generally not lay inside the aviary, preferring to conceal their eggs outside. You must try to provide somewhere for your peahens to lay and sit where they will not be vulnerable to foxes or other predators. This could be a summerhouse, shed or stable but you can't force them to nest in a particular place except in the aviary if you close the door. Once she decides on a nest site the peahen will use it year after year if it is left undisturbed.

If you do find that a peahen has nested somewhere where she will be vulnerable to foxes, there are several precautions you can take. When the bird has left the nest to feed and drink, take away half her eggs, replacing them with dummy ones then put the 'robbed' eggs under a broody hen. This will ensure that you get at least some chicks from that brood if the peahen gets taken by the fox. There are also a few preventative measures you can take which may help. Put a small portable radio near the nest and leave it turned on all night, but don't forget to replace or recharge the batteries regularly. Alternatively, you could use a fox repellant called Renadine, (available from Gamekeepa Feeds Ltd.) which is a vile smelling liquid that you sprinkle round the nest; a more natural repellant is human urine so you could also try peeing round the relevant area each night while the peahen is sitting!

Indian Blue peahen with chicks in an aviary

Breeding in an aviary

Here you will have to provide as natural a habitat as possible and the larger the aviary is the better. Green peafowl have to breed in aviaries because of their wandering habits and also because they are more aggressive than the Blues. Their aviary needs to be away from other aviaries and birds or screened from them with hedges or fencing panels. A Green cock will not mate or settle if he can see another cock bird, but will spend his time pacing up and down peering through the wire.

In general, peahens will not nest in small aviaries but will drop their eggs anywhere. If this happens the eggs will have to be collected each day and hatched in an incubator or under a broody hen. You can try to persuade your peahens to nest by organizing a good choice of secret, hidden places in your aviary so that they feel they can hide their eggs safely. Use a variety of materials such as straw bales, grasses, fir or Cupressus branches to make the nesting sites, but avoid putting them under the perches for obvious reasons. As mentioned before, you may find that several hens all choose to lay in the same nest. If you see a peahen pacing up and down inside the wire looking longingly through to the other side, this is a sure sign that she is ready to lay.

Peahens lay every other day, normally in the late afternoon or early evening. The laying period is from May to August for Indians and a little shorter for Greens. Indian peafowl lay 20 to 25 eggs in a season and Greens lay 15 to 20. One Indian hen is recorded as having laid 32 eggs in one season. Birds in aviaries lay more if the eggs are collected regularly than those allowed to make their own nest and go broody.

The colour of Green peafowl eggs varies from cinnamon to light brown, sometimes with brown mottling. They are larger than those of the Indian peafowl which are a pale creamy buff. Some birds can be identified by the colour of their eggs.

You can make your own dummy eggs from infertile ones that have been blown; pour in liquid plaster of Paris or Artex ceiling compound and let it dry.

Indian peafowl can be kept more intensively than Greens during the breeding period. The Greens must be penned up into groups in November/December to give them plenty of time to settle down before the season starts. The ratio of males to females can be 1 cock and up to 4 hens for Greens and more for Indians, but the norm is 1 to 2 or 1 to 3 for both species.

When your Greens are penned up and settled, don't try to add any more females as they will be either bullied or ostracised by the rest of the birds in the pen.

Six weeks before the start of the breeding season you must increase the protein ratio in your breeding birds' food by putting them onto game or turkey breeder pellets which are at least 18% protein. Partridge breeder pellets, 22% protein, are recommended for Greens.

Some birds, particularly the Greens can become quite aggressive during this period so you may need to take a stick or dustbin lid with you when you go into the aviary.

Chapter 12
Food

Peafowl are omnivores but their main diet in the wild is seeds and insects. One reference I found stated that a peacock's crop was full of hot pepper seeds!

The diet that you will feed to your peafowl is composed of three quarters of mixed corn, (that is wheat, oats and cut maize) and one quarter of pheasant or turkey maintenance pellets (18% protein) together with mixed grit (crushed limestone, flint and seashells).

It's also very beneficial for your birds to give them some variety from time to time in the form of cooked pasta or rice, crushed garlic, sultanas, peanuts or salad, cooked vegetables or potatoes, fruit, peas or chopped carrots. They will love any of these and it's easy to see why some peacocks hang round picnic tables!

Self-feed treddle hopper which keeps the food dry and the wild birds out. The peafowl stands on the foot plate to open the hopper.

Day old chicks must be fed with pheasant or turkey starter crumbs (27% protein) until they are 3 weeks old. They then progress to pheasant or turkey mini pellets (24.5% protein) until week 8 when they change to pheasant or turkey grower pellets (21% protein) until week 16. At week 12 start to introduce some wheat into the food and gradually build this up over the next 4 weeks until you are feeding 50% wheat and 50% pellets. At 18 to 24 weeks the young adults can be switched over to the adult maintenance diet.

From 12 weeks onwards mixed grit should be available all the time.

The rearing pellets you give your birds normally contain a coccidiostat (anti-coccidiosis drug) but no Emtryl (Dimetridazole) or anti-blackhead drug; this is now banned but can be obtained on prescription from your vet and is a water soluble compound.

If you use water soluble drugs against Blackhead, Coccidiosis or Sinusitus mix them in a measuring jug and then pour into the birds' empty water container. When the treatment period is over wash out the water containers before filling them with fresh water.

Indian Blue peacock

Chapter 13
Diseases in Peacocks

Peafowl are very hardy birds providing they are kept in the right way and are fed a balanced diet with appropriate vitamin supplements.

They are members of the pheasant/chicken family and as such are vulnerable to their diseases, but because peafowl are normally kept non-intensively the range of ailments that they can contract is much smaller. Having said that, beware of problems such as E-colis, Salmonella and Aspergillosis when rearing young peafowl intensively. If you are worried about the health of your birds, you can always refer to our book in the Gold Cockerel Series, "Poultry and Waterfowl Problems".

These are the main diseases and ailments that you may encounter in peafowl:

Blackhead (Histomoniasis)

This disease frequently occurs when peafowl mingle with hens, turkeys or pheasants. It affects young poults and adults which look mopey and discharge a bright yellow diarrhoea. They can die within 2 to 10 days so act fast. The treatment for this is Emtryl (Dimetridazole) which you put in the birds' water. Emtryl has actually been withdrawn by Brussels because it was found to be carcinogenic but it is still available in small quantities for pigeon and dove keepers or from your local vet on prescription.

Coxy (Coccidiosis)

This is mainly seen in young poults when they are put out to grass, but it can occur in adults as well. It frequently develops in wet weather and is often found in damp litter in the rearing house. The birds become quiet and mopey and discharge white diarrhoea (sometimes milky, sometimes watery). They gradually become weaker and die.

Clean out your birds' living quarters and spray with disinfectant. Move your peafowl into a clean run with short grass, and treat them with a water soluble coccidiostat like Baytox. Most growers pellets have a coccidiostat incorporated in the mix.

Sinusitus (Mycoplasmosis)

This is a respiratory disease, and some birds seem to be more prone to it than others. It starts with bubbly foam in the corner of the eye then progresses to swellings, soft at first, under one or both eyes. The discharge from this is foul smelling. The disease is spread via the drinking water and by the birds sneezing. Treat it with Baytril which is probably the best drug, or water soluble Tylan or Tiamvitin or injections of Tylan. Although these drugs certainly suppress the disease, it does have a habit of re-occurring.

Bumblefoot

This is caused by peafowl jumping down from roosts or perches and landing badly. It can also develop from a cut in the bird's foot. A swelling will appear round the ankle, toe or foot pad and can lead to lameness. This is why it is important to have a good bed of shavings in the accommodation house and sand under the perches in the aviary. Treat-

Bumblefoot on a bird's toe

ment is normally a jab of penicillin, but this is a difficult area and often the lameness disappears while the swelling remains.

Frost bite

This affects the bird's toes; they turn black and become very brittle and will eventually fall off leaving short stumps. If you live in a part of the country where the cold can be very severe you will have to build some properly insulated winter accommodation to avoid this problem. Make the perches 10cms (4") across, then the perching peafowl can bury their feet in their feathers at night, and a heat lamp in the roosting area will also help.

Worms

There are no physical signs of this unless you have a bird with gape worm who literally gapes. Birds with a heavy worm burden lose a lot of weight and can be very listless. It also affects their appetite and they can be either quite uninterested in food or else ravenously hungry. The droppings will be greenish.

There are several types of worm, round worms, tape worms or caecal worms which live in the caecal tracts and the intestines. The gape worm lives in the wind pipe and can cause a bird to gasp and struggle for breath.

Fortunately all these worms can be treated with Flubenvet (Flubendazole), a powder which is added to the food. It is sensible to worm your peafowl regularly twice a year whether or not you think they have a problem.

Fleas and Lice

Most birds have a few of these external parasites which normally do no harm but can sometimes become a serious burden. This is where a dust bath comes in very useful to help control the problem.

Red Mite

These live and breed in perch sockets and any nooks and crannies inside the birds' accommodation. They can be seen as red or white clusters and come out to suck blood from the birds as they perch at night. There are sprays on the market to deal with these pests.

Newcastle Disease

It's important to remember that peafowl can also contract Fowl Pest (Newcastle Disease).

Index

A 6th century Coptic frieze showing a peacock in the Coptic Museum, Cairo, Egypt

Useful Addresses

Gamekeepa Feeds Ltd. Southerly Park, Binton, Nr. Stratford upon Avon, Warwickshire, CV37 9TU
Tel: 01789 772429

Quinton Spratt, peafowl breeder and supplier,
Homestead Farm, Forncett St. Mary, Norwich, Norfolk, NR16 1JP
Tel: 01508 489471

U.P.A. United Peafowl Association Inc. PO Box 24, Klingerstown, PA 17941, U.S.A.
Tel: (570) 425 3364

W.P.A. World Pheasant Association, PO Box 5, Lower Basildon, Reading, Berkshire, RG8 9PF

NOTES

NOTES